HANS CHRISTIAN ANDERSEN TALES

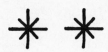

Illustrated by Kai C.
Translated from the Danish text by R. P. Keigwin

SKANDINAVISK BOGFORLAG · FLENSTEDS FORLAG
ODENSE DENMARK

Published in co-operation with
Hans Christian Andersen Museum
Odense

Printed by Nørhaven Bogtrykkeri a/s, Viborg
ISBN 87-7501-158-1

Contents

The Red Shoes

There was once a little girl, very delicate and pretty, and yet so poor that in summer she always had to go barefooted and in winter she had to wear big wooden clogs which chafed her insteps most horribly, until they were quite red.

In the middle of the village lived a shoemaker's widow, who had some strips of old red cloth, and out of these she did her best to sew a little pair of shoes. They were rather clumsy-looking shoes, but the old widow meant well; they were for the little girl, whose name was Karen. As it happened, she got the red shoes and put them on for the first time on the very day that her mother was buried. Of course they weren't exactly the right shoes for a funeral, but they were the only ones she had; and so she wore them on her bare feet, as she followed the humble straw coffin.

Just then a large old-looking carriage drove up with a large old-looking lady inside it. She caught sight of the little girl and felt sorry for her. So she said to the parson: "Look here, If you let me have the little girl, I'll take care of her."

Karen thought this was all because of the red shoes, but the old lady said they were hideous and had them burnt; Karen herself was given nice new clothes and was taught to read and sew. People said how pretty she was, but the looking-glass said to her: "You are more than pretty, you are lovely."

On one occasion the Queen was passing through the country with her little daughter, who was a Princess. People flocked around the castle, and Karen was there too; and the little Princess shewed herself at one of the windows. She was wearing a beautiful white dress; no train nor golden crown, but lovely red morocco shoes—far, far prettier than the ones the shoemaker's widow had made for little Karen. No, there was really nothing in the world like red shoes.

By now Karen was old enough to be confirmed. She was given new clothes, and she was also to have new shoes. The best shoemaker in town took the measurement of her feet in his own private room, where there were big glass cabinets with elegant shoes and shiny boots. They made a brave show, but the old lady's sight was far from good, and so it gave her no pleasure. Among the shoes was a red pair just like the ones the Princess had been wearing—oh, they were pretty! The shoemaker explained that they had been made for an earl's daughter but didn't quite fit. "That must be patent leather from the way they shine," said the old lady.

"Yes, don't they shine!" said Karen; and as they were a good fit, the shoes were bought. But the old lady didn't realise that they were red, for she would never have allowed Karen to go to Confirmation in red shoes. And yet that's just what happened.

Everybody stared at her feet and, as she walked up the aisle to the chancel, she felt that even the old pictures over the tombs, those portraits of the clergy and their wives in stiff ruffs and long black gar-

6

ments, were fastening their eyes on the red shoes. It was these that filled her head and spoke of holy baptism, of the covenant with God, and of her duty now to become a fully-fledged Christian. And the organ played so solemnly, and the children sang so beautifully, and the old choirmaster sang, too; but Karen thought of nothing but her red shoes.

By the afternoon, sure enough, the old lady had heard from everybody about the shoes being red, and she said how shocking it was; they were quite out of place and in future, when Karen went to church, she must always wear black shoes, however old they were.

Next Sunday there was Communion, and Karen looked at the black shoes, and she looked at the red shoes . . . And then she looked at the red ones again—and put the red ones on.

It was a beautiful sunny day. Karen and the old lady took the path through the cornfield, where it was a bit dusty. At the churchdoor stood an old soldier with a crutch and a funny long beard which was more red than white—in fact, it really was red. He made a deep bow to the old lady and asked if he might dust her shoes. And when Karen also put out her foot, "My! what lovely dancingshoes!" said the soldier. "Stay on tight when you dance!" and he gave the soles a tap with his hand.

The old lady gave the soldier something for himself and went with Karen into the church. The whole congregation stared at Karen's red shoes, and so did all the portraits; and when Karen knelt before the altar and put the gold chalice to her lips, she thought of nothing but the red shoes—it seemed as if they were floating in front of her. She forgot to sing the hymns, and she forgot to say the prayers.

Presently everyone came out of church, and the old lady stepped into her carriage. As Karen raised her foot to get in after her, the old soldier, who was standing close by, said: My! what lovely dancing-shoes!" Karen couldn't resist—she had to dance a few steps and, once she had started, her feet went on dancing just as though the shoes had some power over them. She danced round the corner of the church—she couldn't stop; the coachman had to run after her and pick her up and carry her back into the carriage. But still her feet went on dancing and gave the kind old lady some dreadful kicks. At last they got them off, and her legs kept still.

When they came home, the shoes were put away in a cupboard, but Karen still kept taking a peep at them. By and by the old lady fell ill; it was said she would never get better. She had to be nursed and cared for, and nobody was more suited for this than Karen. But a big ball was being given in the town, and Karen was invited. She looked

8

at the old lady, who after all couldn't live long, and she looked at the red shoes. She couldn't see there would be any harm. She put on the red shoes, she had a perfect right to do that . . . But then she went to the ball and began to dance.

But when she wanted to go to the right, the shoes went dancing off to the left; and when she wanted to go up the room, the shoes went dancing down the room—down the stairs through the street and out by the town-gate. Dance she did and dance she must, away into the dark forest.

Up among the trees she saw something shining. It looked like a face, and so she thought it was the moon; but it was the old soldier with the red beard, sitting and nodding and saying: "My! what lovely dancing-shoes!"

This made her frightened, and she tried to kick off the red shoes, but they still stuck on tight. She tore off her stockings, but the shoes had grown fast to her feet, and so dance she did and dance she must, over field and furrow, in rain and sun, by night and day; but the night-time was the worst.

She danced into the open churchyard, but the dead there didn't dance; they had something better to do. She wanted to sit down by the poor man's grave, where the bitter tansy grew, but peace and quiet were not for her and, when she danced towards the open church-door, she found an angel there in long white robes and with wings reaching from his shoulders to the ground. His face was stern and solemn, and in his hand he held a sword with broad shining blade.

"Dance you shall," said the angel, "dance in your red shoes until you are cold and pale, until your skin shrivels up like a skeleton's! Dance you shall from door to door, and at all the houses where the

children are vain and proud you shall knock till they hear you and are frightened. You shall dance, you shall dance . . ."!

"Mercy! Mercy!" cried Karen. But she never heard the angel's answer, for the shoes whirled her away through the gate and the field, along highway and byway, dancing, dancing, all the time.

One morning she danced past a door she knew well. From inside came the sound of a hymn; then out came a coffin all covered with flowers. She realised then that the old lady was dead, and she felt that now she was deserted by everyone, as well as cursed by the angel of God.

Dance she did and dance she must, dance on in the dark night . . . The shoes whirled her away over thorns and stubble, until she was scratched and bleeding. She danced across the heath up to a lonely little house. She knew that the executioner lived here, and she rapped the window-pane with her knuckles and said: "Please come out! I can't come in, because I'm dancing."

"Do you mean to say you don't know who I am? I cut off wicked people's heads—my goodness, how my axe is quivering!"

"Please don't cut off my head!" said Karen, "for then I can't show that I'm sorry for my sins. Cut off my feet with the red shoes."

10

Then she confessed all her sins, and the executioner cut off her feet with the red shoes. But the shoes went dancing with the little feet across the fields into the depths of the forest. And he made her wooden feet and crutches; he taught her a hymn—the Psalm for Sinners—and she kissed the hand that had wielded the axe and went her way across the heath.

"Surely by now I must have done penance for the red shoes," she said. "I'll go to church and let everyone see me." And she did; she went quickly towards the church-door but, when she reached it, there were the red shoes dancing in front of her, and she grew frightened and turned back.

All the next week she was miserable and did nothing but cry, but when Sunday came round she said to herself: "Dear me, I really feel I've been through enough. Surely I'm just as good as many of those that sit so perkily there in church." And she plucked up her courage and started off, but she got no further than the gate, when she saw the red shoes dancing in front of her, and she grew frightened and turned back and repented deeply of her sins.

Next she made her way to the parsonage and asked to be taken in there as a servant; she would work so hard and do her very best. She never gave a thought to the wages, only that she might have a roof over her head and be with kind people.

The parson's wife felt sorry for her and took her into her service and found her hard-working and sensible. In the evenings Karen sat and listened in silence, while the parson read aloud from the Bible. All the little ones were very found of her but, when there was talk of dress and finery and of being as pretty as a picture, she would shake her head.

The following Sunday they all went to church, and they asked her to go with them; but with tears in her eyes she looked sadly at her crutches and, when the others went off to hear the word of God, she went alone to her tiny room, where there was just enough space for a bed and a chair, and here she sat devoutly reading her prayerbook. As she did so, the wind brought the sound of the organ to her from the church, and her eyes filled with tears as she lifted up her face, exclaiming: "Help me, O God!"

Then the sun came out so brightly, and straight in front of her stood the same angel in white robes that she had seen that night at the church-door. But instead of the sharp sword he was holding a beautiful green bough that was covered with roses; and he touched the ceiling with it so that it arched itself higher, and where he touched it there shone a golden star. And he touched the walls so that they grew wider; and she saw the organ which was still playing, she saw the old pictures of the clergy and their wives, and the congregation sitting in the carved pews and singing from their hymn-books ... You see, the church itself had come to the poor girl in her narrow little room—or was it she who had come to the church? She was sitting in the pew with all the others from the parsonage and, when they had finished the hymn and looked up from their books, they nodded to her and said: "It was right you should come, Karen." "It was God's mercy!" she answered.

And the organ pealed forth and the young voices of the choir sounded so soft and pure. The bright warm sunshine streamed in through the church-window to the place where Karen was sitting. Her heart was so full of sunshine and peace and joy that at last it broke, and her soul flew on the sunbeams to heaven, where there was no one to ask about the red shoes.

12

The Nightingale

You know of course that in China the Emperor is a Chinese and his subjects are Chinese too. The story I'm going to tell you happened many years ago, but that's just why you had better hear it now before it's forgotten.

The Emperor's palace was the finest palace in the world, made entirely of delicate porcelain. It was all so precious and fragile that you had to be tremendously careful how you touched anything. The garden was full of the rarest flowers, and the loveliest of these had little silver bells tied to them which tinkled so that no one should go by without noticing them. Yes, everything in the Emperor's garden was most carefully thought out, and it stretched so far that even the gardener had no idea where it ended. If you kept on walking, you found yourself in a glorious wood with tall trees and deep lakes. The wood went right down to the sea, which was blue and deep; big ships could sail right in under the branches of the trees. Here lived a nightingale that sang so beautifully that even the poor fisherman, who had so much else to see to, would stop and listen, when he was taking his nets in at night and suddenly heard the nightingale. "My word! that's lovely!" he said; but then he had to get on with his work and forgot about the bird. Yet when she sang again the following night and the fisherman was out there with his nets, "My word!" he repeated, "that is lovely!"

From every country in the world travellers came and marvelled at the Emperor's great city, his palace and his garden; but as soon as they heard the nightingale, everyone said the same—"Oh, but that's the best of all!" And when they got home from their travels, they had many tales to tell, and clever people wrote books about the city and the palace and the garden, yet they never forgot the nightingale; she was given the place of honour. And the poets wrote the most lovely poems, all about the nightingale in the wood there beside the deep sea.

These books went all over the world, and so in course of time some of them reached the Emperor. There he sat in his golden chair, reading and reading; and now and then he nodded his head, for he was pleased to come across such splendid descriptions of the city and the palace and the garden. "But the nightingale is really the best of all", said the book he was reading.

"What's this?" thought the Emperor. "The nightingale? Why, I've never heard of her! Is there such a bird in my Empire and, what's more, in my own garden? Nobody's ever told me that—one has to read about it in a book!" And, with that, he summoned his gentleman-in-waiting, who was so grand that, whenever anyone of lower rank than himself ventured to speak to him or to ask a question, he only answered "P!"—and that means nothing at all.

"It says here that we have a most remarkable bird called a nightingale", said the Emperor. "They declare that there's nothing like her in all my Empire. Why have I never been told of this before?"

14

"It's the first I've ever heard of her," answered the gentleman-in-waiting. "She's never been presented at Court."

"I command her to be brought here this evening to sing to me," said the Emperor. "The whole world knows what I possess—and I know nothing!"

"It's the first I've ever heard of her," repeated the gentleman-in-waiting. "I shall look for her, and I shall find her."

Find her? But where? The gentleman-in-waiting ran upstairs and downstairs, through rooms and passages, but none of the people he met had ever heard of the nightingale. So the gentleman-in-waiting hurried once more to the Emperor and said it was obviously a story invented by those who write books. "Your Majesty mustn't believe everything you read. Most of it's just made up—what they call the black art."

"But the book I read it in," said the Emperor, "was sent me by the high and mighty Emperor of Japan, so it can't be untrue. I *will* hear the nightingale. She's to come and sing to-night, under my royal patronage; and if she fails to appear, then every courtier shall be punched in the stomach directly after supper."

"Tsing-pe!" said the gentleman-in-waiting and ran up and down all the stairs again, through all the rooms and passages; half the Court ran with him, for they didn't a bit like the idea of being punched in the stomach. They kept asking after this extraordinary nightingale that everybody knew about except the people at Court.

At last they came across a poor little girl in the kitchen, who said "Oh, golly—the nightingale? I know her well. My, how she can sing! Every evening I'm allowed to take home a few scraps from the table for my poor sick mother who lives down by the shore; and on my way back I often take a rest in the wood, and then I hear the nightingale singing. It brings tears to my eyes, just as if my mother were kissing me."

"Little kitchen-maid," said the gentleman-in-waiting, "you shall have a regular situation in the kitchen and be allowed to watch the Emperor eating his dinner, if only you'll take us to the nightingale. You see, she's to give a command performance this evening before the Emperor."

So then they all set out for the wood where the nightingale used to sing; half the Court joined in the quest. As they were going along, a

cow began to moo. "Ah, there she is!" said the courtiers. "What remarkable strength in such a small creature! Yes, it's certainly not the
first time we've heard her."

"No, but that's a cow mooing," said the little kitchen-maid. "We've still got a long way to go."

Then some frogs started croaking in the pond. "Delightful!" said the Emperor's chaplain. "Now I can hear her: just like little church-bells."

"No, those are frogs," said the little kitchen-maid. "But I expect we shall soon hear her now". And then the nightingale began to sing.

"There she is!" said the little girl. "Listen, listen! There she is, up there"—and she pointed to a little grey bird up in the branches.

"Is it possible?" said the gentleman-in-waiting. "Why, I never pictured her like that. How ordinary she looks! I expect she's off colour through having so many distinguished visitors."

"Little nightingale," called out the small kitchen-maid quite boldly, "our gracious Emperor would like you to sing to him."

18

"With the greatest of pleasure," said the nightingale, and at once began to sing most deliciously.

"Just like glass bells," observed the gentleman-in-waiting. "And look at the way her little throat keeps working. I can't make out why we've never heard her before. She'll make a great hit at Court."

"Shall I sing once more to the Emperor?" asked the nightingale, for she thought the Emperor was there.

"My excellent little nightingale," replied the gentleman-in-waiting, "it is my very pleasant duty to summon you to a concert this evening at the palace, where you will enchant His Imperial Majesty with your delightful singing."

"It sounds best out in the open," said the nightingale. Still, she went along readily enough on hearing it was the Emperor's wish.

19

At the palace everything had been polished up, until the china walls and floors glittered in the light of thousands and thousands of gold lamps. The loveliest flowers, hung ready for tinkling, were arranged in the corridors; and there was such a draught from the scurrying to and fro that their bells were all set ringing and you couldn't hear a word that was spoken.

In the middle of the great hall in which the Emperor sat was a golden perch for the nightingale. The entire Court was present; and the little kitchen-maid was allowed to stand behind the door, as she now ranked as a regular palace kitchen-maid. Everyone was dressed in their finest clothes, and they all looked at the little grey bird as the Emperor nodded to her to begin.

And the nightingale sang so beautifully that tears came into the Emperor's eyes and trickled right down his cheeks; and then the nightingale's singing became even lovelier—it went straight to his heart. And the Emperor was so pleased that he said the nightingale should have his gold slipper to wear round her neck; but the nightingale said no thank you, she had been rewarded enough already. "I've seen tears in the Emperor's eyes; that's my richest reward. There's a strange power in an Emperor's tears. Heaven knows, they are reward enough!" And then the nightingale let them hear her lovely voice again.

"Who ever saw such airs and graces!" said the ladies around; and they went and filled their mouths with water so as to gurgle when anyone spoke to them; yes, they thought they could be nightingales too. Even the lackeys and lady's maids expressed their approval; and that's saying a good deal, for they are the most difficult of all to satisfy. There's no doubt whatever, the nightingale made a great hit.

She was now to remain at Court and have her own cage, with leave

20

to go out for two walks in the daytime and one at night. She was given twelve attendants, who each held on tightly to a silk ribbon fastned round her leg. There was absolutely no fun in a walk like that.

The whole city was talking of this remarkable bird, and, when two people met, one of them merely said "night" and the other "gale", and after that they sighed and quite understood each other. What's more, eleven grocers' children were named after her, but not one of them had a note in its head . . .

One day a large parcel arrived for the Emperor, with the word "Nightingale" written on the outside.

"I expect this is a new book about our famous bird," said the Emperor. But it wasn't a book at all; it was a little gadget lying in a box —an artificial nightingale that was supposed to look like the live one but was covered all over with diamonds, rubies and sapphires. You only

had to wind it up, and it could sing one of the songs that the real nightingale sang; and all the while its tail went up and down, glittering with silver and gold. Round its neck was a little ribbon, on which was written: "The Emperor of Japan's nightingale is poor beside the Emperor of China's."

"How delightful!" they all said; and the one who brought the artificial bird was at once given the title of Chief Imperial Nightingale Bringer.

22

"Now they must both sing at once," suggested somebody. "What a duet that will be!"

So the two birds had to sing together; but it wasn't a success, because the real nightingale sang in her own way, whereas the artificial bird went by clockwork. "It can't be blamed for that", said the Master of the Emperor's Music. "It keeps perfect time and follows my own methods exactly." After that, the artificial bird had to sing by itself. It was just as popular as the real one, and of course it was also much prettier to look at, glittering there like a cluster of brooches and bracelets.

Over and over again it sang its one and only song—thirty-three times without tiring—and the listeners would have liked to hear it all once more, but the Emperor thought that now it was time for the real nightingale to do some singing . . . But where ever was she? No one had noticed her fly out of the open window, away to her own green woods.

"Bless my soul, what's the meaning of this?" said the Emperor; and all the courtiers were highly indignant and said what an ungrateful creature the nightingale was. "Still, we've got the best one," they added; and then the artificial bird was obliged to sing once more. That was the thirty-fourth time they were hearing the same song; but they didn't quite know it even yet, for it was so difficult. And the Master of Music gave the bird extraordinary praise; in fact, he declared that it was better than the real nightingale, not merely because of its outward appearance and all the wonderful diamonds, but also for the works inside.

"You see, ladies and gentlemen and, above all, Your Imperial Majesty, with the real nightingale there's no telling what's going to happen. But with the artificial bird everything is fixed beforehand. Such-and-such will be heard and no other. One can account for it all: one can open it up and show the human mind at work, the position of the cylinders, how they go round, and the way in which one thing follows from another!"

Everyone said that they quite agreed, and the Master of Music got permission to show the bird to the public on the following Sunday. "They must also hear it sing," said the Emperor. And hear it they did. They were as delighted as if they had drunk themselves merry on tea— and that's so like the Chinese! They all said "Oh!" and held up one finger—the finger we call "lick-pot"—and nodded their heads. But the poor fisherman who had heard the real nightingale said: "It don't sound so bad—quite like the bird—and yet there's something kind o' missing."

The real nightingale was sent into exile—banished from land and realm. The artificial bird had its place on a silk cushion close to the Emperor's bed; all the presents it had been given, gold and precious stones, lay round about, and it was promoted to be Chief Imperial

Bedside Minstrel of the First Class on the Left; for the Emperor considered the side on which the heart lies to be the most distinguished, and even an Emperor has his heart on the left. The Master of Music wrote a book in twenty-five volumes about the mechanical bird; it was very long and learned, full of the most difficult Chinese words, and everyone pretended they had read it and understood it, or else of course they would have been thought stupid and got punched in the stomach.

Well, this went on for a whole year, until the Emperor, his Court and all the other Chinese knew by heart every little gurgle in the throat of the artificial songbird; but for that very reason they came to like it all the better. They could join in singing themselves, and they did. The street-boys sang "zee-zee-zee, kloo-kloo-kliik!" and the Emperor sang it, too! It really was tremendous fun.

But one evening, just as the artificial bird was in full song and the Emperor lay listening in bed, something went "snap!" inside the bird. Then there was a "whirrrr"; the wheels all went whizzing round . . . and the music stopped.

The Emperor quickly jumped out of bed and sent for the doctor, but what could he do? Then they brought along the watchmaker, and after a great deal of talk and poking about he got the bird to work after a fashion; but he said that it mustn't be used too often, as the bearings were almost worn out and it was impossible to get fresh parts that would fit in properly with the music. This was a sad disappointment. Once a year only was the artificial bird allowed to sing, and even that was something of a strain; but on these occasions the Master of Music made a little speech full of difficult words, saying that the bird was just as good as ever—and so of course it was just as good as ever.

Five years had now gone by, and presently the whole country was filled with sorrow, for really in their hearts they were all fond of their Emperor; but now he was ill and not likely to live, it was said. A new Emperor had already been chosen, and people stood out in the street and asked the gentleman-in-waiting how their Emperor was. "P!" he replied and shook his head.

Cold and pale lay the Emperor in his magnificent great bed. The whole Court believed him to be dead, and each of them hastened to pay their respects to the new Emperor. The valets ran out to gossip about it, and the palace housemaids had a large tea-party. Everywhere, in all the rooms and corridors, heavy cloth had been laid down in order to deaden the sound of footsteps; the whole palace was as still as still could be.

But the Emperor wasn't dead yet. Stiff and pale he lay in the magnificiant bed with its long velvet curtains and heavy gold tassels; through an open window high up on the wall the moon was shining down on the Emperor and the artificial bird.

The poor Emperor could scarcely breathe; it was just as if something was sitting on his chest. He opened his eyes, and then he saw it was Death that sat on his chest and had put on his gold crown and was holding the Emperor's gold sword in one hand and his splendid banner in the other. All round the bed, from the folds in the great velvet curtains, strange faces were peering, some of them hideous, others wonderfully gentle and kind. They were the Emperor's good and evil deeds, gazing down on him now that Death was sitting on his heart.

"Do you remember that?" they whispered, one after the other. "Do you remember that?" And they told him so much that the sweat stood out on his forehead.

26

"I never realised that," said the Emperor. "Music, music! Sound the great Chinese drum," he cried, "to save me from hearing what they say!"

But still they went on, and Death kept nodding like a Chinese at every word they whispered.

"Music, music!" shrieked the Emperor. "You wonderful little golden bird, sing, I implore you, sing! I've given you gold and precious stones, I've hung my own gold slipper round your neck—sing, I implore you, sing!"

But the bird was silent; there was no one to wind it up, and it couldn't sing without that. But Death went on staring at the Emperor with his great hollow eyes, and everything was so still, so terribly still.

All at once, close to the window, came a burst of most beautiful singing. It was the little live nightingale, perched in a tree outside. She had heard of her Emperor's distress and had therefore come to sing him consolation and hope; and, as she sang, the shapes grew fainter and fainter, the blood in the Emperor's weak limbs ran faster and faster, and Death himself listened and said, "Go on, little nightingale, go on!"

"Yes, if you'll give me the fine gold sword . . . if you'll give me the splendid banner . . . if you'll give me the Emperor's crown!"

And Death gave up each treasure for a song, and still the nightingale went on singing. She sang of the quiet churchyard where the white roses bloom, where the elder-tree smells so sweet, and where the fresh grass is watered with the tears of those who are left behind. Then Death began to long for his garden and floated like a cold white mist out of the window.

"Thank you, thank you!" said the Emperor. "You heavenly little

28

bird, now I know who you are! I banished you from land and realm—and yet you have sung those evil visions away from my bed, you have lifted Death from my heart. How can I ever repay you?"

"You have done already", said the nightingale. "The first time I sang I brought tears to your eyes—I shall never forget that. Those are the jewels that rejoice a singer's heart ... But sleep now and get well and strong again! I will sing to you."

And the nightingale sang, and the Emperor fell into a sweet sleep— such a peaceful, refreshing sleep. When he awoke, restored once more to health, the sun was shining in through the windows. None of his servants had come back yet, for they thought he was dead; but the nightingale was still singing outside.

"You must never leave me again", said the Emperor. "You shall only sing when you want to, and the artificial bird—I shall break it into a thousand pieces."

"No, don't do that," said the nightingale. "It's done what it could; don't part with it yet. I can't make my home in the palace, but let me come when I feel that I want to; then I'll sit of an evening on this branch by the window, and my singing can make you both gay and thoughtful. I shall sing of those that are happy, and of those that suffer; I shall sing of the good and the evil that are here lurking about you. Your little songbird must fly round to distant homes—to the poor fisherman and the humble peasant—to those who are far from you and your Court. I love your heart better than your crown . . . and yet there's a breath of something holy about the crown . . . I shall come, I shall sing to you; yet there's one thing you must promise me."

"Whatever you ask!" answered the Emperor, standing there in the imperial robes that he had himself put on and holding the heavy gold sword to his heart.

"One thing only I ask of you. Let no one know that you have a little bird who tells you everything; that will be best." And then the nightingale flew away.

The servants came in to look after their dead Emperor. Yes, there they stood and the Emperor said, "Good morning!"

The little Matchseller

It was terribly cold. Snow was falling, and soon it would be quite dark; for it was the last day in the year—New Year's Eve. Along the street, in that same cold and dark, went a poor little girl in bare feet—well, yes, it's true, she had slippers on when she left home; but what was the good of that? They were great big slippers which her mother used to wear, so you can imagine the size of them; and they both came off when the little girl scurried across the road just as two carts went whizzing by at a fearful rate. One slipper was not to be found, and a boy ran off with the other, saying it would do for a cradle one day when he had children of his own.

So there was the little girl, walking along in her bare feet that were simply blue with cold. In an old apron she was carrying a whole lot of matches, and she had one bunch of them in her hand. She hadn't sold anything all day, and no one had given her a single penny. Poor mite, she looked so downcast, as she trudged along hungry and shivering. The snowflakes settled on her long flaxen hair, which hung in pretty curls over her shoulders; but you may be sure she wasn't thinking about her

31

looks. Lights were shining in every window, and out into the street came the lovely smell of roast goose. You see, it was New Year's Eve; that's what she was thinking about.

Over in a little corner between two houses—one of them jutted out rather more into the street than the other—there she crouched and huddled with her legs tucked under her; but she only got colder and colder. She didn't dare to go home, for she hadn't sold a match nor earned a single penny. Her father would beat her, and besides it was so cold at home. They had only the bare roof over their heads and the wind whistled through that, although the worst cracks had been stopped up with rags and straw. Her hands were really quite numb with cold. Ah, but a little match—that would be a comfort. If only she dared pull one out of the bunch, just one, strike it on the wall and warm her fingers! She pulled one out . . . ritch! . . . how it spirted and blazed! Such a clear warm flame, like a little candle, as she put her hand round it—yes, and what a curious light it was! The little girl fancied she was sitting in front of a big iron stove with shiny brass knobs and brass facings, with such a warm friendly fire burning . . . why, whatever was that? She was just stretching out her toes, so as to warm them too, when—out went the flame, and the stove vanished. There she sat with a little stub of burnt-out match in her hand.

She struck another one. It burned up so brightly, and where the gleam fell on the wall this became transparent like gauze. She could see right into the room, where the table was laid with a glittering white cloth and with delicate china; and there, steaming deliciously, was the roast goose stuffed with prunes and apples. Then, what was even finer, the goose jumped off the dish and waddled along the floor with the carving-knife and fork in its back. Right up to the poor little girl it

came ... but then the match went out, and nothing could be seen but the massive cold wall.

She lighted another match. Now she was sitting under the loveliest Christmas tree; it was even bigger and prettier than the one she had seen through the glass-door at the rich merchant's at Christmas. Hundreds of candles were burning on the green branches, and gay-coloured prints, like the ones they hang in the shopwindows, looked

33

down at her. The little girl reached up both her hands . . . then the match went out; all the Christmas candles rose higher and higher, until now she could see they were the shining stars. One of them rushed down the sky with a long fiery streak.

34

"That's somebody dying," said the little girl; for her dead Grannie, who was the only one who had been kind to her, had told her that a falling star shows that a soul is going up to God.

She struck yet another match on the wall. It gave a glow all around, and there in the midst of it stood her old grandmother, looking so very bright and gentle and loving. "Oh, Grannie", cried the little girl, "do take me with you! I know you'll disappear as soon as the match goes out—just as the warm stove did, and the lovely roast goose, and the wonderful great Christmas-tree". And she quickly struck the rest of the matches in the bunch, for she did so want to keep her Grannie there. And the matches flared up so gloriously that it became brighter than broad daylight. Never had Grannie looked so tall and beautiful. She took the little girl into her arms, and together they flew in joy and splendour, up, up, to where there was no cold, no hunger, no fear. They were with God.

But in the cold early morning huddled between the two houses, sat the little girl with rosy cheeks and a smile on her lips, frozen to death on the last night of the old year. The New Year dawned on the little dead body leaning there with the matches, one lot of them nearly all used up. "She was trying to get warm", people said. Nobody knew what lovely things she had seen and in what glory she had gone with her old Grannie to the happiness of the New Year.

The Top and the Ball

A top and a ball were in a drawer together with some other toys, and then one day the top said to the ball: "Look here, we live together in the same drawer—shall we become engaged?" But the ball, who was made of morocco leather and fancied herself quite as much as any smart young lady, wouldn't even answer such a ridiculous question.

Next day the little boy whom the toys belonged to came and painted the top red and yellow all over and hammered a brass nail into the middle of it. The top was really a fine sight, as it went spinning round and round.

"Look at me!" said the top to the ball. "What do you say now? Don't you think after all we might be engaged? We go so splendidly together: you bounce and I dance. There couldn't be a happier couple than us two."

"Oh, you think that, do you?" answered the ball. You don't seem to realise that my father and mother were morocco slippers and that I have a cork inside me."

"Ah, but I'm made of mahogany," said the top. "Why, the mayor turned me himself on his own lathe, and he was so pleased about it."

"Am I really expected to believe that?" asked the ball.

"May I never be whipped again, if I'm not telling you the truth!" answered the top.

"You give a very fine account of yourself," said the ball. "But I really must say no. You see, I'm what you might call half-engaged to a swallow. Every time I go up in the air, he pops his head out of the nest and says: 'Will you? Will you?' I've already said to myself that I will, and that's as good as a half-engagement. But I promise never to forget you."

"A lot of good that'll be!" replied the top; and they said no more to each other.

Next day the ball was taken out into the garden. The top watched how she flew high up into the air, just like a bird, until she went clean out of sight. But she came back again each time and, whether from longing or because she had a cork inside her, this was always followed by a high bounce as soon as she touched the ground. The ninth time the ball went up, she never came back; the little boy looked and looked, but she had vanished.

"Ah, I could tell him where she is," said the top with a sigh. "She's in the swallow's nest and has married the swallow."

The more the top thought it all over, the more he lost his heart to the ball. The mere fact that he couldn't have her made him love her more than ever; the strange thing was that she should have accepted anyone else. And the top went on dancing and spinning round, but all the time he was thinking about the ball, who grew more and more beautiful in his imagination. In this way several years went by, till gradually it became nothing more than an old love-affair . . .

But, although the top was no longer young, suddenly one day he found himself painted all over with gold. Never had he looked so handsome; he was now a gold top, and he whirled and whirled until he hummed. Gosh! It was something like! Then all at once he jumped too high—and disappeared. They looked and looked, even down in the basement, but he was not to be found.

Whereever had he got to?

He had jumped into the dustbin among all sorts of cabbage-stalks, sweepings and rubbish that had come down from the gutter on the roof.

"Here's a nice place for me to come to!" said the top. My gold paint will soon go off and—did you ever see such riff-raff as I've got around me!" And then he peeped sideways at a long skinny-looking cabbage-stalk and a curious round object that looked like an old apple . . . But it wasn't an apple at all, it was an old ball that had been lying up in the gutter on the roof for several years and become quite sodden.

"Thank goodness, here's someone at last of one's own class that one can talk to," said the ball, with a glance at the gilded top. "Actually I'm made of marocco leather, stitched by gentlewomen, and I've got a cork inside me, but nobody would ever think so to look at me. I was just going to marry a swallow, when I landed up in the gutter; and there I've been for five years growing more and more sodden. That's a long time, believe me, for a young lady."

But the top didn't say a word. His thoughts went back to his old sweetheart, and the longer he listened the more certain he became that this was her.

Presently the maidservant came to clear out the dustbin. "Well, I never! Here's the gold top!" she said. Back in the house the top came in for lots of attention, but nothing was said about the ball, and the top never spoke again of his old love. Love is, of course, bound to fade away, when your sweetheart has spent five years growing sodden in a gutter; you can't be expected to know her again, if you meet her in a dustbin.

The Ugly Duckling

Summer-time! How lovely it was out in the country, with the wheat standing yellow, the oats green, and the hay all stacked down in the grassy meadows! And there went the stork on his long red legs, chatter-

ing away in Egyptian, for he had learnt that language from his mother. The fields and meadows had large woods all around, and in the middle of the woods there were deep lakes.

Yes, it certainly was lovely out in the country. Bathed in sunshine stood an old manor-house with a deep moat round it, and growing out of the wall down by the water were huge dock-leaves; the biggest of them were so tall that little children could stand upright underneath. The place was as tangled and twisty as the densest forest, and here it was that a duck was sitting on her nest. It was time for her to hatch out her little ducklings, but it was such a long job that she was beginning to lose patience. She hardly ever had a visitor; the other ducks thought more of swimming about in the moat than of coming and sitting under a dock-leaf just for the sake of a quack with her.

At last the eggs cracked open one after the other—"peep! peep!"—and all the yolks had come to life and were sticking out their heads.

"Quack, quack!" said the mother duck, and then the little ones scuttled out as quickly as they could, prying all round under the green leaves; and she let them do this as much as they liked, because green is so good for the eyes.

"Oh, how big the world is!" said the ducklings. And they certainly had much more room now than when they were lying in the egg.

"Do you suppose this is the whole world?" said their mother. "Why, it goes a long way past the other side of the garden, right into the parson's field; but I've never been as far as that. Well, you're all out now, I hope"—and she got up from her nest—"no, not all; the largest egg is still here. How ever long will it be? I can't bother about it much more." And she went on sitting again.

42

"Well, how's it going?" asked an old duck who came to pay a call.

"There's just this one egg that's taking such a time," said the sitting duck. "It simply won't break. But just look at the others—the loveliest ducklings I've ever seen. They all take after their father—the wretch! Why doesn't he come and see me?"

"Let's have a look at the egg which won't crack," said the old duck. "I'll bet it's a turkey's egg. That's how I was bamboozled once. The little ones gae me no end of trouble, for they were afraid of the water —fancy that!—I just couldn't get them to go in. I quacked and clacked, but it was no good. Let's have a look at the egg . . . Ay, that's a turkey's egg, depend upon it! Let it be, and teach the others to swim."

"I think I'll sit just a little while yet," said the duck. "I've been sitting so long that it won't hurt to sit a little longer."

"Please yourself!" said the old duck, and away she waddled.

At last the big egg cracked. There was a "peep! peep!" from the young one as he tumbled out, looking so large and ugly. The duck glanced at him and said: "My! what a huge great duckling that is! None of the others look a bit like that. Still, it's never a turkey-chick, I'll be bound . . . Well, we shall soon find out. He shall go into the water, if I have to kick him in myself!"

The next day the weather was gloriously fine, with sun shining on all the green dockleaves. The mother duck with her whole family came down to the moat. Splash! into the water she jumped. "Quack, quack!" she said, and one after another the ducklings plomped in after her. The water closed over their heads, but they were up again in a moment and floated along so beautifully. Their legs worked of their own accord, and now the whole lot were in the water—even the ugly grey duckling joined in the swimming.

"It's no turkey, that's certain," said the duck. "Look how beautifully he uses his legs and how straight he holds himself. He's my own little one all right, and he's quite handsome, when you really come to look at him. Quack, quack! Now, come along with me and let me show you the world and introduce you all to the barnyard, but mind and keep close to me, so that nobody steps on you; and keep a sharp look-out for the cat."

— Then they made their way into the duck-yard. There was a fearful noise going on, for there were two families fighting for an eel's head, and after all it was the cat that got it.

"You see! That's the way of the world," said the mother duck and licked her bill, for she too had fancied the eel's head. "Now then, where are your legs?" she said. "Look slippy and make a nice bow to the old duck over there. She's the most genteel of all these; she has Spanish blood, that's why she's so plump. And do you see that crimson rag she wears on one leg? It's extremely fine; it's the highest distinction any duck can win. It's as good as saying that there is no thought of getting rid of her; man and beast are to take notice! Look alive, and don't turn your toes in! A wellbred duckling turns its toes out, like father and mother . . . That's it. Now make a bow and say 'quack!'"

They all obeyed; but the other ducks round about looked at them and said out loud: "There! Now we've got to have that rabble as well —as if there weren't enough of us already! Ugh! What a sight that duckling is! We can't possibly put up with him"—and one duck immediately flew at him and bit him in the neck.

"Leave him alone," said the mother. "He's doing no one any harm."

"Yes, but he's so gawky and peculiar," said the one that had pecked him, "so he'll have to be squashed."

44

"What pretty children you have, my dear!" said the old duck with the rag on her leg. "All of them but one, who doesn't seem right. I only wish you could make him all over again."

"No question of that, my lady," said the ducklings' mother. "He's not pretty, but he's so good-tempered and he can swim just as well as the others—I dare say even a bit better. I fancy his looks will improve as he grows up, or maybe in time he'll grow down a little. He lay too long in the egg—that's why he isn't quite the right shape." And then she plucked his neck for him and smoothed out his feathers. "Anyhow, he's a drake, and so it doesn't matter so much," she added. "I feel sure he'll turn out pretty strong and be able to manage all right."

"The other ducklings are charming," said the old duck. "Make yourselves at home, my dears, and if you should find such a thing as an eel's head, you may bring it to me."

And so they made themselves at home.

But the poor duckling who was the last out of the egg and looked so ugly got pecked and jostled and teased by ducks and hens alike. "The great gawk!" they all clucked. And the turkey, who was born with spurs and therefore thought himself an emperor, puffed up his feathers like a ship under full sail and went straight at him, and then he gobble-gobbled till he was quite red in the face. The poor duckling didn't know where to turn; he was terribly upset over being so ugly and the laughing-stock of the whole barnyard.

That's how it was the first day, and afterwards things grew worse and worse. The poor duckling got chivied about by all of them; even his own brothers and sisters treated him badly, and they kept saying: "If only the cat would get you, you ridiculous great guy!" And the mother herself wished he were far away. The ducks nipped him, the hens pecked him, and the maid who had to feed the poultry let fly at him with her foot.

After that, he ran away and fluttered over the hedge, and the little birds in the bushes grew frightened and flew into the air. "That's because I'm so ugly," thought the duckling and closed his eyes—and yet managed to get away. Eventually he came out to the great marsh where the wild-ducks lived and lay there all night, utterly tired and dispirited.

46

In the morning the wild-ducks flew up and looked at their new companion. "What ever are you?" they asked, and the duckling turned in every direction and bowed as well as he could.

"What a scarecrow you are!" said the wild-ducks, "but that won't matter to us, as long as you don't marry into our family." Poor thing! He wasn't dreaming of getting married; all he wanted was to be allowed to stay quietly among the rushes and drink a little marsh-water. After he had been there for two whole days, two wild-geese came along—or rather two wild-ganders, for they were both males. It was not long since they were hatched; that's why they were so perky.

"Look here, my lad!" they began. "You are so ugly that we quite like you. Will you come in with us and migrate? Not far off, in another marsh, are some very nice young wild-geese, none of them married, who can quack beautifully. Here's a chance for you to make a hit, ugly as you are."

"Bang! bang!" suddenly echoed above them, and both the ganders fell down dead in the rushes, and the water became red with blood. "Bang! bang!" sounded once more, and flocks of wild-geese flew up from the rushes, so that immediately fresh shots rang out. A big shoot was on. The party lay ready all round the marsh; some even sat up in the trees and hung far over the water. Splashing through the mud came the gun-dogs, bending back reeds and rushes this way and that. It was terrifying for the poor duckling, who was just turning his head round to bury it under his wing when he suddenly found close beside him a fearsome great dog with lolling tongue and grim, glittering eyes. It lowered its muzzle right down to the duckling, bared its sharp teeth and —splash! it went off again without touching him.

The duckling gave a sigh of relief. "Thank goodnes, I'm so ugly that even the dog doesn't fancy the taste of me." And he lay there quite still, while the shot pattered on the reeds and crack after crack was heard from the guns.

It was late in the day before everything was quiet again, but the poor duckling didn't dare to get up yet; he waited several hours longer before he took a look round and then made off from the marsh as fast as he could go. Over field and meadow he scuttled, but there was such a wind that he found it difficult to get along.

Towards evening he came up to a poor little farm-cottage; it was so broken-down that it hardly knew which way to fall, and so it remained standing. The wind whizzed so fiercely round the duckling that he had to sit on his tail so as not to be blown over. The wind grew worse and worse. Then he noticed that the door had come off one of its hinges and hung so much on the slant that he could slip into the house through the crack. And that's just what he did.

There was an old woman living here with her cat and her hen. The cat, whom she called Sonny, could arch its back and purr; it could even give out sparks, if you stroked its fur the wrong way. The hen had such short little legs that it was called Chickabiddy Shortlegs; it was a very good layer, and the woman loved it like her own child.

Next morning they at once noticed the strange duckling, and the cat started to purr and the hen to cluck. "Why, what's up?" said the woman, looking round. But her sight wasn't very good, and she took the duckling for a fat duck that had lost its way. "My! What a find!" she said. "I shall be able to have duck's eggs—as long it isn't a drake! We must give it a trial."

And so the duckling was taken on trial for three weeks; but there was no sign of an egg. Now, the cat was master in the house and the

48

hen was mistress, and they always used to say "We and the world,"
because they fancied that they made up half the world—what's
more, much the superior half of it. The duckling thought there might
be two opinions about that, but the hen wouldn't hear of it.

"Can you lay eggs?" she asked.

"No."

"Well, then, hold your tongue, will you!"

And the cat asked: "Can you arch your back or purr or give out sparks?"

"No."

"Well, then, your opinion's not wanted, when sensible people are talking."

And the duckling sat in the corner, quite out of spirits. Then suddenly he remenbered the fresh air and the sunshine, and he got such a curious longing to swim in the water that—he couldn't help it—he had to tell the hen.

"What's the matter with you?" she asked. "You haven't anything to do—that's why you get these fancies. They'd soon go, if only you'd lay eggs or else purr."

"But it's so lovely to swim in the water," said the duckling; "so lovely to duck your head in it and dive down to the bottom."

"Most enjoyable, I'm sure," said the hen. "You must have gone crazy. Ask the cat about it—I've never met any one as clever as he is —ask him if he's fond of swimming or diving! I say nothing of myself. Ask our old mistress, the wisest woman in the world! Do you suppose that she's keen on swimming and diving?"

"You don't understand me," said the duckling.

"Well, if we don't understand you, I should like to know who would. Surely you'll never try and make out you are wiser than the cat and the mistress–not to mention myself. Don't be silly, child! Give thanks to your Maker for all the kindness you have met with. Haven't you come to a nice warm room, where you have company that can teach

50

you something? But you're just a stupid, and there's no fun in having you here. You may take my word for it—if I say unpleasant things to you, it's all for your good; that's just how you can tell which are your real friends. Only see that you lay eggs and learn how to purr or give out sparks!"

"I think I'll go out into the wide world," said the duckling.

"Yes, do," said the hen.

And so the duckling went off. He swam in the water; he dived down, but none of them would have anything to do with him because of his ugliness.

Autumn now set in. The leaves in the wood turned yellow and brown, the wind seized them and whirled them about, while the sky above had a frosty look. The clouds hung heavy with hail and snow, and the raven who perched on the fence kept squawking "ow! ow!— he felt so cold. The very thought of it gave you the shivers. Yes, the poor duckling was certainly having a bad time.

One evening, when there was a lovely sunset, a whole flock of large handsome birds appeared out of the bushes. The duckling had never seen such beautiful birds, all glittering white with long graceful necks. They were swans. They gave the most extraordinary cry, spread out their magnificent long wings and flew from this cold country away to warmer lands and open lakes.

They mounted high, high up into the air, and the ugly duckling felt so strange as he watched them. He turned round and round in the water like a wheel and craned his neck in their direction, letting out a cry so shrill and strange that it quite scared even himself. Ah! he could never forget those beautiful, fortunate birds; and directly they were lost to sight he dived right down to the bottom and, when he came up again, he was almost beside himself. He had no idea what the birds were called, nor where they were flying to, and yet they were dearer to him than any he had ever known; he didn't envy them in the least—how could he ever dream of such loveliness for himself? He would be quite satisfied, if only the ducks would just put up with him, poor gawky-looking creature!

52

What a cold winter it was! The duckling had to keep swimming about in the water to prevent it freezing right up. But every night the pool he was swimming in grew smaller and smaller; then the ice froze so hard that you could hear it creaking. The duckling had to keep his feet moving all the time to prevent the water from closing up. At last he

grew faint with exhaustion and lay quite still and finally froze fast in the ice.

Early next morning he was seen by a peasant who went out and broke the ice with his wooden clog and carried the duckling home to his wife. And there they revived him.

54

The children wanted to play with him, but the duckling was afraid they meant mischief and fluttered in panic right up into the milkbowl, so that the milk slopped over into the room. The woman screamed out and clapped her hands in the air, and then he flew into the butter-tub, and from there down into the flour-bin, and out of it again. Dear, dear, he did look an object! The woman screamed at him and hit at him with the tongs, and the children tumbled over each other trying to catch him—how they laughed and shouted! . . . It was a good thing the door was open; the duckling darted out into the bushes and sank down, dazed, in the new-fallen snow.

But it would be far too dismal to describe all the want and misery the duckling had to go through during that hard winter . . . He was sheltering among the reeds on the marsh, when the sun began to get warm again and the larks to sing; beautiful spring had arrived.

Then all at once he tried his wings; the whirr of them was louder than before, and they carried him swiftly away. Almost before he realised it; he found himself in a big garden with apple-trees in blossom and sweet-smelling lilac that dangled from long green boughs right over the winding stream. Oh, it was so lovely here in all the freshness of spring! And straight ahead, out of the thicket, came three beautiful white swans, ruffling their feathers and floating so lightly on the water. The duckling recognised the splendid creatures and was overcome with a strange feeling of melancholy.

"I will fly across to them, those royal birds! They will peck me to death for daring, ugly as I am, to go near them. Never mind! Better to be killed by them than be nipped by the ducks, pecked by the hens, kicked by the girl who minds the poultry, and suffer hardship in winter." And he flew out on to the water and swam towards the beautiful swans. As they caught sight of him, they darted with ruffled feathers to meet him. "Yes, kill me, kill me!" cried the poor creature and bowed his head to the water awaiting death. But what did he see there in the clear stream? It was a reflection of himself that he saw in front of him, but no longer a clumsy greyish bird, ugly and unattractive—no, he was himself a swan!

It doesn't matter about being born in a duckyard, as long as you are hatched from a swan's egg.

He felt positively glad at having gone through so much hardship and want; it helped him to appreciate all the happiness and beauty that were there to welcome him . . . And the three swans swam round and round and stroked him with their beaks.

Some little children came into the garden and threw bread and grain into the water, and the smallest one called out: "There's a new swan!" and the other children joined in with shouts of delight: "Yes, there's a new swan!" And they clapped their hands and danced about and ran to fetch father and mother. Bits of bread and cake were thrown into the water, and everyone said: "The new one is the prettiest—so young and handsome!" And the old swans bowed before him.

This made him feel quite shy, and he tucked his head away under his wing—he himself hardly knew why. He was too, too happy, but not a bit proud, for a good heart is never proud. He thought of how he had been despised and persecuted, and now he heard everybody saying that he was the loveliest of all lovely birds. And the lilacs bowed their branches to him right down to the water, and the sunshine felt so warm and kindly. Then he ruffled his feathers, raised his slender neck and rejoiced from his heart: "I never dreamed of so much happiness, when I was the ugly duckling."

It's Absolutely True

"It's a terrible affair!" said a hen—speaking, too, in quite another part of the town from where it all happened. "It's a terrible affair about that chicken-house. I daren't sleep alone tonight. It's a good thing there are so many of us roosting together." And then she told them her story, which made the other hen's feathers stand on end and even set the cock's comb drooping. It's absolutely true!

But let's begin at the beginning. It was in a chicken-house at the other end of the town. The sun went down, and the hens flew up. One of them was a white short-legged bird, who regularly laid her eggs and was altogether a most respectable hen. When she got to her perch she preened herself with her beak, and a little feather came out and went fluttering down. "So much for that one!" she said. "The more I preen, the lovelier I shall grow, no doubt!" Of course it was only said in fun, because she was the fun-maker among the hens, though in other ways (as you've just heard) most respectable. After that, she went off to sleep.

All about was quite dark; hen sat with hen, but the one next to her was still awake. She had heard, and had not heard—as you must often do in this world, if you are to live in peace and quiet. And yet she couldn't help saying to the hen perched on the other side of her, "Did you hear that? I give no names, but there is a hen who means to pluck out her feathers for the sake of her looks. If I were a cock, I'd simply despise her."

Now directly above the hens sat the owl, with her owl husband and her owl children. They had sharp ears in that family; they could hear every word their hen neighbour said; and they rolled their eyes, and the owl mother fanned herself with her wings. "Don't take any notice—but of course you heard what she said, didn't you? I heard it with my own ears, and they're going to hear a lot before *they* drop off. One of the hens has so far forgotten what is fit and proper for a hen that she's calmly plucking out all her feathers in full view of the cock."

"*Prenez garde aux enfants!*" said the father owl. "Not in the children's hearing!"

"But I must tell the owl over the way; she's so highly respected in our set." And away flew the mother.

"Tu-whit, tu-who!" they both hooted, and it carried right down to the doves in the dovecot across the yard. "Have you heard, have you heard? Tu-who! There's a hen that' plucked out all her feathers for the sake of the cock. She'll freeze to death, if she isn't dead already, tu-who!"

"Where, ooh, where?" cooed the doves.

"In the yard opposite. I as good as saw it with my own eyes. Really the story's almost too improper to repeat; but it's absolutely true."

"Tr-rue, tr-rue, every wor-rd!" said the doves; and they cooed down to their hen-run, "There's a hen, some say there are *two,* who have plucked out all their feathers so as to look different from the others

58

and to attract the attention of the cock. It's a risky thing to do; suppose they catch cold and die of fever ... Yes, they're dead—*two* of them."

Then the cock joined in: "Wake up, wake up!" he crowed, and flew up on to the wooden fence. His eyes were still sleepy, but he crowed away all the same; "Three hens have died of love for a cock; they had plucked out all their feathers. It's a horrible story—I don't want it–pass it on!" "Pass it on!" squeaked the bats; and the hens clucked and the cocks crowed, "Pass it on, pass it on!" And so the story flew from one hen-house to another, till at last it came back to the place where it had really started.

"There are five hens"—that's how it ran—"who have all pluck-ed out their feathers to show which of them had got thinnest for love of the cock. Then they pecked at each other till the blood came and they all fell down dead, to the shame and disgrace of their family and the serious loss of their owner."

The hen that had lost the one loose little feather didn't of course recognise her own story and, as she was a respectable hen, she said, "How I despise those hens!—though there are plenty more just like them. That's not the kind of thing to be hushed up, and I shall do my best to get the story into the papers, so that it may go all over the country. It'll serve those hens right, and their family too."

And into the papers it came—all there in print—and it's absolutely true: *"One little feather can easily become five hens!"*

Willie Winkie

Nobody in the world knows so many stories as Willie Winkie ... And he knows how to tell them, too—no doubt about that!

Late in the evening, when children are sitting nice and quietly at a table or on their stools, that's when Willie Winkie comes along. He comes ever so softly up the stairs, for he goes in his stocking-feet, and he very gently opens the door. Then fft! he squirts sweet milk into the children's eyes—only the tiniest drop, yet always enough to stop them keeping their eyes open—and so they don't see him. He steals up just behind them and gently blows down their necks, and then their heads grow heavy. It's all right—it doesn't hurt them, because Willie Winkie is really most kind to children, and for that it's best to get them to bed. They must be quite still before he can tell them stories.

When at last the children are asleep, Willie Winkie sits down on the bed. He's nicely dressed, and his coat's made of some sort of silk—though it's hard to say what colour it is, for as he turns about it's all shot with green and red and blue. Under each arm he carries an umbrella. One umbrella, with pictures on it, he holds over the good children, so that they have the loveliest dreams all night; and the other umbrella, without anything on it, he holds over the naughty children, so that they sleep like logs and when they wake in the morning haven't dreamt a thing.

Now you shall hear how Willie Winkie came every night for a whole week to a little boy called Hjalmar, and the stories he told him. There are seven stories altogether, for there are seven days in the week.

Monday

"Now look here!" said Willie Winkie one evening, when he had got Hjalmar to bed. "First. I'm going to smarten things up"—and straight away all the flowers in the flower-pots became large trees stretching their long branches up under the ceiling and along the walls, until the whole room was turned into a lovely bower, and all the branches were full of blossom; every flower was prettier than a rose, with a delicious smell, and, if you cared to taste it, was sweeter than jam. The fruit all glistened like gold, and there were buns that were bursting with currants—you never saw anything like it! But all at once there began a most dreadful hullabaloo over in the drawer where Hjalmar kept his school-books.

"What's up now?" said Willie Winkie, as he went over to the table and opened the drawer. It was the slate that was in such distress, because a wrong figure had got into the sum so that it wouldn't come right. The pencil frisked and gambolled at the end of its string like a little dog; it wanted to help the sum, but didn't know how to.

Next, there was a howling set up from inside Hjalmar's copybook— it was simply ghastly to listen to! Running down every page were all the capital letters, each with a small letter beside it, a complete row of

62

them the whole way down. They acted as a copy, and beside them were also some letters which imagined that they looked like the copy ones; Hjalmar had written these, and they straggled about almost as if they had tumbled over the ruled line they were supposed to stand on.

"Look here, this is how you ought to hold yourselves," said the copy. "Look—sloping a bit like this, with a free swinging stroke."

"Ah, we should so like to," said Hjalmar's letters, "but we can't; we're feeling so bad."

"Then you must have a dose of medicine!" said Willie Winkie.

"Oh, no!" they screamed—and at once stood up as straight as you could wish for.

"There! That's enough story-telling for the present," said Willie Winkie. "Now I must put them through their drill—left, right—left, right!" And he drilled the letters until they stood up as firm and straight as any copy ones. But after Willie Winkie had gone and Hjalmar looked at them the next morning, they were just as miserable-looking as before.

Tuesday

Directly Hjalmar was in bed, Willie Winkie touched all the furniture in the room with his little magic squirt, and they immediately began to chatter. They all chattered about themselves, except the spittoon, which stood in silent annoyance that the others could be so conceited as to talk and think only of themselves and never have a thought for the one who, after all, stood so modestly in the corner and let himself be spat upon.

Over the chest of drawers hung a large painting in a gilt frame. It showed a landscape with tall venerable trees, flowers growing in the

64

meadow, and a great broad stream curving round behind a wood, past many a castle, far out into the open sea.

Willie Winkie touched the painting with his magic squirt, and the birds in it at once began to sing. The branches stirred in the trees, and the clouds scudded along; you could see their shadow drifting over the fields.

Willie Winkie took little Hjalmar and lifted him up to the picture-frame, and Hjalmar put his feet into the picture, right into the tall grass; there he stood, with the sun shining down on him through the branches of the trees. He ran down to the water and got into a little boat that was lying there. It was painted red and white, and its sails shone like silver. Six swans, all with gold crowns down over their necks and a glittering blue star on their heads, towed the boat past the green woods, where the trees were telling tales about robbers and witches, and the flowers had stories of the dear little elves and of all they had heard from the butterflies.

The loveliest fishes, with scales like gold and silver, swam after the boat, leaping up now and then so that there was an answering splash in the water; and the birds flew behind in two long rows, red birds and blue birds, big ones and little ones. The gnats kept dancing round and the cockchafer repeated his "boom! boom!—they all wanted to go with Hjalmar, and each of them had a story to tell.

Yes, it was a wonderful sail they went for. At one moment the woods were quite thick and dark, and then suddenly they were like a beautiful garden with flowers and sunshine, and there appeared great castles of glass and marble with princesses on the balconies who were all little girls that Hjalmar knew well and had played with. They reached out their hands, and each one was holding the nicest sugar-pig any sweet-shop could sell. Hjalmar caught hold of one end of a sugar-pig as he sailed past, and the princess held on tight to the other, so they each got a piece; she got the smallest and Hjalmar much the biggest. Little princes, with gold swords carried at the salute, were on guard at every castle, and they showered him with toffee and tin soldiers; they were proper princes!

Sometimes Hjalmar was sailing through forests, and sometimes through what seemed to be immense halls or through the middle of a town. In this way he came to the home of the nurse who had looked after him when he was quite small. She had been so very fond of him, and now she nodded and waved her hand, singing the pretty verses she had made up herself and sent to Hjalmar.

66

Of you, dear Hjalmar, I often think
   and how as a babe I kissed you
on forehead and mouth and cheek so pink—
   my darling, how much I've missed you!
Your earliest words I heard you crow,
   but soon from your side was driven.
God grant you his blessing here below,
   sweet messenger sent from heaven!

And all the birds joined in her songs; the flowers danced on their stalks, and the old trees nodded, just as if Willie Winkie were telling them stories too.

Wednesday

Goodness! how the rain was coming down outside! Hjalmar could hear it in his sleep, and when Willie Winkie opened a window, the water came right up to the sill. There was a complete lake outside, but a splendid-looking ship lay alongside the house.

"Hjalmar, my boy, will you come for a sail?" asked Willie Winkie. "Then you'll be able to go off to foreign parts to-night and be back again in the morning."

And all of a sudden Hjalmar found himself standing in his Sunday best on board the splendid ship, and the weather at once became fine. She sailed through the streets, cruised round the church and finally came out into open sea. On and on they sailed, until the land was quite out of sight; and they came upon a flock of storks, who were also leaving home and were bound for the warm countries. They were flying one behind the other and had already flown a very long way. One of the storks was so tired that his wings could hardly bear him up any longer; he was the very last in the row, and he soon got a long way behind. Finally he sank with outspread wings lower and lower; he gave a few more beats with his wings, but that was no good; and then his feet touched the ship's rigging, he glided down the sail and plomp! there he was on the deck.

Then the ship's boy picked him up and put him in the hen-coop among hens, ducks and turkeys. The poor stork looked so sorry for himself amongst them.

"What a creature!" said all the hens.

And the turkey-cock puffed himself out as big as he could and asked who he was, and the ducks waddled backwards and nudged each other —"Quick, get quacking!"

Then the stork told about the warmth of Africa, and the pyramids, and the ostrich that ran like a wild horse through the desert; but the ducks never understood what he was saying and so they nudged each other again—"We all agree, don't we, that he's a stupid?"

"As stupid as can be!" said the turkey-cock with a gobble-gobble. At that the stork kept silent and thought about his beloved Africa.

"Those are nice lanky legs you have," said the turkey. "How much a yard?"

"Quack, quack, quack!" chuckled the ducks. But the stork pretended not to hear.

"You may as well join in the laugh", said the turkey to him; "it was very neatly put. Or was it perhaps too low for him? Heigh-ho! He's a bit one-eyed; we must look to ourselves, if we want to have some fun." And they clucked away, and the ducks kept quack-quack-quacking— it was terrible how funny they seemed to think it was.

68

But Hjalmar went over to the hen-coop, opened the door and called to the stork, who then hopped out on to the deck. He had now had a good rest and seemed to give Hjalmar a nod, in order to thank him. The next moment he spread out his wings and flew off to the warm countries. But the hens went on clucking and the ducks went on quacking, while the turkey-cock became quite red in the face.

"To-morrow we shall make soup of you!" said Hjalmar—and then he woke up. There he was, laying in his little bed. It really was an astonishing voyage Willie Winkie had arranged for him that night.

"What do you think I've got here?" said Willie Winkie. "Now don't get frightened; I'm going to show you a little mouse"—and there was the dainty little creature in Willie Winkie's hand as he held it out to him. "It has come," he said, "to invite you to a wedding. There are two little mice here tonight who are entering into matrimony. They live down under the floor of your mother's larder; it ought to be a charming affair".

"But how am I to get through the tiny mousehole in the floor?" asked Hjalmar.

"Leave that to me," said Willie Winkie; "I know how to make you small enough." And he touched Hjalmar with his magic squirt, so that he at once became smaller and smaller and at last was no bigger than your finger. "Now we can borrow the tin soldier's clothes; I think they'll fit you, and it looks so smart to be wearing uniform at a party."

"Ra-ther!" said Hjalmar, and the next moment there he was dressed as the most dapper-looking tin soldier.

"If you'll kindly take a seat in your mother's thimble," said the little mouse, "I'll do myself the honour of pulling you along."

"Good gracious! Miss Mouse," said Hjalmar, "to think of me giving you all that trouble!" And off they drove to the mouse-wedding.

First, they made their way in under the floor by a long passage that was just high enough, and no more, for them to be able to drive along in a thimble, and the whole passage was lit up by touchwood.

"Doesn't it smell nice!" said the mouse that was pulling him. "The whole passage has been rubbed with bacon-rind; there's nothing to touch it!"

Now they entered the wedding-chamber. To the right stood all the

little she-mice, twittering and tittering as if they were making fun of each other; to the left stood all the he-mice, stroking their whiskers with their paws. But out in the middle of the floor were the bridal pair, standing in a scooped-out cheese and kissing each other like anything in front of everybody. Well, after all, they were engaged and were going to be married almost at once.

More and more guests kept arriving, and the mice looked like trampling each other to death. The bride and bridegroom had stationed themselves in the middle of the door-way, so there was no getting either out or in. The whole room, like the passage, had been rubbed with bacon-rind, which was all the refreshment there was; but for dessert there was produced a pea in which a mouse belonging to the family had nibbled the name of the bridal pair—or rather, the first letter. That was considered something altogether out of the ordinary.

All the mice agreed that it was a lovely wedding and that they had talked with such interesting people.

Finally, Hjalmar drove home again. He had certainly been in very smart society; on the other hand, he had had to put up with no end of a shrinking, to make himself small enough to get into a tin soldier's uniform.

Friday

"You'd never believe how many elderly people would like to get hold of me," said Willie Winkie. "Especially the ones who've done something they shouldn't. 'Dear, kind Winkie', they say to me, 'We can't shut our eyes at night, and so we lie awake and see our evil deeds sitting on the edge of the bed like hideous little goblins and squirting us with hot water. Do come and chase them away, so that we can get a good sleep!' And then they add with a deep sigh, 'We're only too glad to pay. Good-night, Winkie—the money's in the window'. But I don't do it for money," said Willie Winkie.

"Now, what are we going to have to-night?" asked Hjalmar.

"Well, I don't know if you'd care to go to another wedding—quite a different sort to yesterday's, I may say. Your sister's big doll—the one that looks like a man and is called Herman—is to marry the doll Bertha; and, as it's Bertha's birthday, there will be a lot of presents."

"Yes, I know what that means!" said Hjalmar. "Whenever the dolls want new clothes, my sister lets them have a birthday or a wedding. That must have happened a hundred times."

"Well, but to-night's wedding is the 101st time, and when Number

72

101 is over there won't be any more. That's why it's going to be so brilliant. Just look!"

And Hjalmar looked across at the table. There stood the little cardboard house with lights in the windows, and all the tin soldiers were presenting arms outside. The bride and bridegroom were seated on the floor, leaning up against the leg of the table and looking very thoughtful, as indeed they might well do. But Willie Winkie draped himself in Grannie's black petticoat and married them! When the wedding was over, all the furniture in the room joined in singing the following beautiful song, which had been written by the pencil and went to the tune of the devil's tattoo:—

Our song shall greet like wind and weather

these two that the priest has tied together;

so poker-stiff they stand in tether,

each of them made of chamois leather!

    Hurrah for bride and groom together!

    Hurrah for them both in wind and weather!

Next came the wedding presents; they had said they would rather not have any eatables, as their love was enough for them to live on.

"Which do you think?" said the bridegroom to his bride. "Shall we go and stay in the country, or shall we travel abroad?" They asked advice of the swallow, who was a great traveller, and of the old hen, who had hatched five broods of chicks. The swallow described the lovely warm countries, where the grapes hang in big heavy bunches and the air is so soft and the colour on the hills is something quite unknown to us here.

"Still, they haven't got our garden cabbage!" said the hen. "I once spent the summer with all my chicks in the country; there was a gravel pit we could go and scratch in, and then we had the use of a garden where there were cabbages—such a green, they were! I can't imagine anything lovelier."

"But one cabbage-stalk looks just like another," said the swallow. "And then again, the weather here is so often bad."

"Oh, well, we're used to that," replied the hen.

"But it's so cold. It freezes."

"That just suits the cabbages," said the hen. "Besides, we get warm weather too, sometimes. Don't you remember, only four years ago, we had a summer that lasted five weeks! It was so hot here that you could

74

hardly breathe . . . And then we don't get all those poisonous creatures they have abroad; and we are free from brigands. Anyone who doesn't think our country is the best of all is a scoundrel; he doesn't really deserve to live here"—and tears came into the hen's eyes. "I've done a bit of travelling myself," she added. "I've ridden over 50 miles in a coop. There's no fun at all in travel."

"Yes, the hen's a sensible woman," said the doll Bertha. "I don't want to go mountaineering either. It only means that first you go up and—then you go down. No, let's move out to the gravel pit and go for a walk in the cabbage patch."

And that's how they left it.

Saturday

"Any stories for me to-night?" asked little Hjalmar, as soon as Willie Winkie had got him to bed.

"We haven't time for that this evening," said Winkie, as he opened above him the umbrella with the prettiest pictures on. "Take a peep at those Chinese!"—and the whole umbrella looked like a great Chinese bowl with blue trees and bridges with pointed arches, where there were little Chinese who stood nodding their heads.

"We must have everything trim and tidy for tomorrow," said Winkie. "You see, it's a holy day; it's Sunday. I must go up the church-tower and see if the little church-elves are cleaning the bells, so that they ring out nicely. I must get along to the fields and see if the breezes are blowing the dust off the grass and the leaves. And then—what is really my hardest task—I must have all the stars down and give them a thorough polish. I take them into my apron; but, first, each one of them has to be numbered, and the holes they fit into up there must also be numbered, so that they can find their right places again; otherwise, they wouldn't fit tight and we should get too many shooting stars, as they dropped out one after the other."

"I say, look here, Mr. Winkie," said an old portrait hanging on the wall of Hjalmar's bedroom. "I'm Hjalmar's great-grandfather. Thank you for telling the boy these stories, but you mustn't muddle him with wrong ideas. The stars can't be taken down and polished. A star is a globe, the same as the earth is; that's just the beauty of it."

"Thanks very much, old great-grand-father!" said Willie Winkie. "Thanks very much! You're of course the head of the family—the Grand Old Man—but I'm older than you are. I'm an ancient heathen —the Romans and Greeks call me the Dream God. I visit the very best houses, continually, and I know how to get on with all sorts, both young and old. Now you can tell a story of your own." And Willie Winkie picked up his umbrella and away he went.

"Dear, dear!" said the old portrait. "One mayn't even express one's opinion nowadays."

And at that moment Hjalmar woke up.

"Good evening," said Willie Winkie, and Hjalmar nodded; but then he jumped up and turned his great-grandfather's portrait with its face to the wall, so that it shouldn't butt into the conversation as it did the day before.

"Please tell me some stories: the one about the five peas that lived in a pod, and the one about the cock-a-doodle-doo that made love to the hen-a-doodle-doo, and the one about the darning-needle who was so stuck-up that she fancied she was a sewing-needle!"

"Ah, but one can have too much of a good thing," said Willie Winkie. "I'd rather show you something. I tell you what, I'll show you my brother. He never comes to anyone more than once and, when he comes, he takes them up on his horse and tells them stories. He only knows two: one is so utterly beautiful that no one on earth can imagine it, and the other is so ghastly and terrible—well, it's impossible to describe it."

Then Willie Winkie lifted little Hjalmar up to the window and said, "Look, there's my brother. He's also called Death. You see, he's nothing like so horrid to look at as he is in pictures, where he's nothing but a skeleton. No, he has silver lace on his tunic—it's a splendid hussar uniform with a black velvet cloak flying behind him over his horse. Look how he gallops along!"

And Hjalmar saw how this other Winkie rode away, taking both young and old up on his horse. Some he placed in front of him, others behind; but he always asked them first, "What does it say in your report?" "Good," they all answered. "Ah, but let me see it myself", he said. Then they had to show him the report, and all the ones who had "very good" or "excellent" came to the front seat on the horse and were told the beautiful story. But those who had "moderate" or "poor" had to sit behind and hear the terrible story; they trembled and wept and tried to jump off the horse, but they couldn't do that because they had immediately grown fast on to it.

"But Death is a most wonderful Willie Winkie," said Hjalmar. "I'm not a bit afraid of him."

"No, and you needn't be," said Willie Winkie, "Mind you get a good report, that's all."

"Most instructive!" muttered the great grandfather's portrait. "It does some good, after all, to express one's opinion." And he was quite contented.

There! That's the story of Willie Winkie. Now this evening he can tell you some more himself.

The Tinder Box

Left, right! Left, right! ... Down the country-road came a soldier
marching. Left, right! Left, right! ... He had his knapsack on his back
and a sword at his side, for he had been at the war, and now he was
on his way home. But then he met an old witch on the road. Oh! she
was ugly—her lower lip hung right down on her chest. "Good
evening, soldier," she said, "what a nice sword you've got, and what a
big knapsack! You're a proper soldier! Now I'll show you how to get as
much money as you want!" "Thank you very much, old dame!" said
the soldier.

"Do you see that big tree over there?" said the witch, pointing to a tree near by. "It's quite hollow inside. Now, you must climb right up it, and then you'll see a hole; slip through this, and you'll come down into the tree. I will tie a rope round your waist, so that I can haul you up again, as soon as you give me a shout."

"But what am I to do down in the tree?" asked the soldier.

"Fetch money!" answered the witch. "For, mind you, when you get down to the bottom of the tree, you will find yourself in a large passage. It's quite light there, because hundreds of lamps are burning there. Next, you will see three doors; you can open them all right, for the key's in the lock. If you go into the first room, you will see in the middle of the floor a big chest, with a dog sitting on it which has got eyes as big as tea-cups; but never you mind about that. I'll give you my blue-check apron, and you can spread it out on the floor. Then go along quickly and lift off the dog and put it on my apron; open the lid of the chest and take just as many pennies as you like. They are all copper, but if you would rather have silver, then you must go into the next room. There sits a dog with eyes as large as mill-wheels, but never you mind about that! Put the dog down on my apron, and help yourself to the money! And yet, if it's gold you want, you can get that too—as much as ever you can carry—if only you go into the third room. But this time the dog which is sitting on the money-chest has two eyes each one as big as the Round Tower . . . Something like a dog, I can tell you! But never you mind a bit about that! Just put the dog down on my apron, and then it won't do you any harm, and you can take as much gold out of the chest as you like."

"That doesn't sound at all bad", said the soldier. "But tell me, old witch, what am I to give you? Because I expect you'll be wanting your share!"

80

"No," said the witch, "not a single penny will I take. You've simply got to bring me an old tinder-box that my grandmother forgot, when she was last down there."

"Oh, come on, then! let me get that rope round my middle!" said the soldier.

"Here it is," said the witch, "and here's my blue-check apron."

Then the soldier crawled up the tree, let himself down, plump! through the hole, and now he was standing, as the witch had said, down in the great passage where the hundreds of lamps were burning.

Then he unlocked the first door. Ugh! there sat the dog with eyes as big as tea-cups and glared at him.

"You are a nice chap, you are!" said the soldier. He put it down on the witch's apron and took just as many copper pennies as he could stuff into his pocket. Then he shut the chest, put the dog up again and went into the second room. Bless my soul! there sat the dog with eyes as big as mill-wheels.

"You shouldn't stare at me so!" said the soldier; "you'll strain your eyes." And then he put the dog down on the witch's apron; but when he saw such piles of silver in the chest, he threw away all the coppers he had got and filled up his pockets and his knapsack with nothing but silver. And now he went into the third room! . . . Oh, but it was horrible! The dog in there had actually got two great eyes as big as the Round Tower, and they were going round and round in its head like wheels!

"Good evening!" said the soldier; and he touched his cap, because never in his life had he seen such a dog. But after he had looked at it for a bit, he thought to himself, "Enough of that!" and went and lifted the dog down on to the floor and opened the chest—why, goodness

81

gracious, what a lot of gold there was! There was enough for him to buy the whole of Copenhagen, all the sugar-pigs that the cake-women sell, and all the tin-soldiers and whips and rocking-horses in the world. Yes, yes, plenty of money in there—my word, there was!

So at once the soldier emptied out all the silver coins from his pockets and his knapsack and put in gold instead; yes, and he filled up everything with gold, his pockets, his knapsack, his cap and even his boots, so that he could hardly walk. Now he had got some money! He put the dog back on the chest, slammed the door, and then shouted up through the tree, "Hi, mother! haul me up again, will you?"

"Have you got the tinder-box?" asked the witch.

"Oh no! that's true, I had clean forgotten it," said the soldier; and he went straight back and fetched it. The witch hauled him up out of the tree, and there he was again, standing on the road with his pockets, boots, cap and knapsack bulging with money.

"What are you going to do with this tinder-box?" asked the soldier.

"That's no business of yours!" answered the witch. "You've got your money, now just give me my tinder-box!"

"Rubbish!" said the soldier. "Tell me at once what you want to do with it—or I'll have out my sword and cut your head off."

"No," said the witch.

So he cut off her head . . . There she lay!

But the soldier tied up all his money in her apron and made a bundle of it, to go on his back. He put the tinder-box in his pocket and went straight on into the town.

It was a fine town, and he put up at the finest inn. He ordered the vey best rooms and the food he was most fond of; for, now that he had all that money, he was a rich man. The servant who had to clean his

82

boots thought, well, this was a funny old pair of boots for such a rich gentleman to have; but he hadn't yet bought any new ones. The next day he went out and got some good boots and some really smart clothes. And now the soldier had become quite a fashionable gentleman, and they told him all about the sights of their town, and about their King, and what a pretty Princess his daughter was.

"Where is she to be seen?" asked the soldier.

"She just isn't to be seen," they all answered. "She lives in a big copper castle with lots of walls and towers all round it. No one but the king is allowed to go to her there, because a fortune-teller once said that she is to marry a common soldier, and the king doesn't like that at all."

"My word! I should like to see her," thought the soldier; but of course he couldn't possibly get leave to.

And now he lived a merry life.

He was always going to the theatre, or driving in the Park; and he gave away lots of money to the poor. That was very nice of him; you see, he remenbered so well from the old days how awful it was to be absolutely penniless. But now he was rich and well-dressed, and so he made lots of friends who all said what a fine fellow he was—a real gentleman—and the soldier liked that very much. But as he was spending money every day and never getting any back, at last he had only got twopence left; and so he had to move from the fine rooms he had been living in and go and live in a little poky attic right under the roof. He had to clean his own boots and mend them with a darning-needle, and none of his friends ever came to see him for there were such a lot of stairs to climb.

One evening, when it was quite dark and he couldn't even buy

84

himself a candle, he suddenly remembered that there was a little bit of candle left in the tinder-box that he had got for the old witch out of the hollow tree. So he fetched out the tinder-box and the bit of candle; but just as he was striking a light and the sparks flew up from the flint, the door sprang open, and the dog he had seen down in the tree with eyes as big as tea-cups stood before him and said "What are my lord's commands?"

"I say! said the soldier. "This must be a queer sort of tinder-box, if I can get whatever I want like that." "Bring me some money", he said to the dog; then flick! and away it went, and flick! here it was back again, with a large bagful of pennies in its mouth.

And now the soldier realised what a splendid tinder-box it was. One stroke brought before him the dog which sat on the chest with the copper money; two strokes, the dog with the silver; and three strokes, the dog with the gold. The soldier lost no time in changing back into the fine rooms and the smart clothes, and of course all his friends re-menbered him again at once and were tremendously fond of him.

And then one day he thought to himself "There's something queer about this, that no one's allowed to see the Princess. She's supposed to be so very lovely, according to all these people; but what's the good of that, if she has to sit the whole time inside the copper castle, the one that has all those towers? Can't I possibly manage to see her somehow? Now then, where's my tinder-box?" So he struck a light and flick! there stood the dog with the eyes as big as tea-cups.

"Of course I know it's the middle of the night," said the soldier, "but all the same I would like to se the Princess, that I would! Just for half a jiffy!"

The dog was out of the door in a flash and, before the soldier had

time to think about it, there was the dog again with the Princess lying asleep on his back; and she looked so lovely that anyone could see she was a real princess; and the soldier simply couldn't resist, he had to kiss her—he was a soldier all over.

Then the dog scuttled back again with the Princess, but in the morning, when the King and Queen were at breakfast, the Princess said she had had such a curious dream in the night, about a dog and a soldier. She had ridden on the dog's back, and the soldier had kissed her.

"That's a pretty tale, if you like!" said the Queen.

And so one of the old ladies-in-waiting was told to sit up the following night by the Princess' bed and see if it was really a dream or not.

The soldier did so long for another look at the pretty Princess; and so up came the dog by night and took her and dashed off at full speed. But the old lady-in-waiting put on her overboots and ran just as fast after them, and when she saw them disappear into a big house she thought to herself, "Now I know where it is", and chalked up a big cross on the door. Then she went home to bed, and the dog came back too with the Princess. But when it saw a cross had been chalked on the door where the soldier was living, the dog also took a bit of chalk and put a cross on every door in the town. That was a clever idea, because now, you see, the lady-in-waiting couldn't find the right door, as there were crosses on the whole lot of them.

Early in the morning the King and Queen, the old lady-in-waiting and all the Court officials sallied forth in order to see where it was the Princess had been.

"Here's the house!" said the King, when he saw the first door with a cross on it.

"*No, it's* there, darling!" said the Queen, catching sight of the second door with a cross on it.

"But here's another—and there's another!" they all kept saying. Whichever way they turned, there were crosses on the doors. So then they soon realised that it was no good searching any longer.

But the Queen, you know, was a very clever woman, who could do more than just drive out in a coach. She took her great golden scissors and cut up a large piece of silk and sewed the pieces together into a pretty little bag, which she filled with the finest buckwheat flour. She

fastened the little bag to the Princess's back, and then she snipped a little hole in the bag, so as to sprinkle the flour wherever the Princess went.

At night, up came the dog once more, took the Princess on his back and ran off with her to the soldier, who loved her so dearly and did so wish he were a prince and could marry her.

The dog never noticed how the flour kept leaking out all the way from the castle to the soldier's window, where it ran up the wall with the Princess. The next morning it was quite plain to the King and Queen where their daughter had been going; so they took the soldier and put him in prison.

There he sat. Ugh! how dark and dreary his cell was! And, besides, they kept saying to him "To-morrow you're going to be hanged!" That didn't sound at all cheerful, and the worst of it was he had left his tinder-box at the inn. In the morning, through the iron bars of his little window, he watched people hurrying out of the town to se him hanged. He heard the drums and saw the soldiers marching past. Everyone was afoot. Among them was a cobbler's boy in leather apron and slippers; he was trotting along so fast that one of his slippers came off

88

and flew right against the wall where the soldier sat peeping out be-tween the iron bars.

"I say! you young cobbler, you don't need to hurry like that," the soldier said to him, "they can't begin without me. But look here—if you will kindly run along to where I've been living and fetch me my tinder-box, you shall have twopence for your trouble; but mind you get a move on!" The cobbler's boy was very glad to earn twopence, so he sprinted off for the tinder-box, brought it to the soldier, and—well, now listen to what happened!

Outside the town a high gallows had been built, and round about it stood the soldiers and thousands and thousands of people. The King and Queen sat on a beautiful throne opposite the judge and all his councillors.

Already the soldier had climbed the ladder; but just as they were going to put the rope round his neck he reminded them that, before being executed, a criminal always had the right to ask for one harmless favour. He said he would so like to smoke a pipe of tobacco—after all, it would be the last pipe he could smoke in this world.

Now, the King didn't like to say no to that; so the soldier took his tinder-box and struck a light—one, two, three!—and there stood all three dogs: the one with eyes as big as tea-cups, the one with eyes like mill-wheels, and the one which had eyes as big as the Round Tower.

"Save me now from being hanged!" said the soldier; and then the dogs flew at the judges and all the councillors, and seized some by their legs and others by their noses, and tossed them so high into the air that when they came down they were dashed to pieces.

"I won't be tossed!" said the King; but the biggest dog picked them both up, King and Queen, and sent them hurtling after the others.

Then the soldiers got frightened, and the people all shouted out "Soldier boy, you shall be our King and have the pretty Princess". And they put the soldier into the King's coach, and all three dogs went dancing in front of it and cried out "Hurrah!" And the boys whistled on their fingers, and the soldiers presented arms. The Princess came out of the copper castle and was made Queen, and how pleased she was! The wedding-feast lasted for a week, and the dogs sat at table with everyone else and kept rolling their great big eyes.

90

Simple Simon

Away in the country, in an old manorhouse, lived an old squire. He had two sons who were so clever that—well, the fact is they were too clever by half. They made up their minds to go and propose to the King's daughter; and they had a perfect right to do this, because she had announced that she would marry the man who she thought was best able to speak up for himself.

The two sons now spent a week in preparation. A week was all they were allowed; but it was quite long enough, for they had had a good education, and that is such a help. One of them knew the whole Latin dictionary off by heart, and also the local newspaper for the last three years, both backwards and forwards. The other son had learnt up all the by-laws of the city companies and the things every alderman is supposed to know; he thought this would help him to talk politics with the Princess; and, besides, he knew how to embroider braces, he was so very clever with his fingers.

"I shall win the Princess!" cried both of them; and so their father gave them each a beautiful horse. The brother who had learnt off the dictionary and the newspapers got a coal-black horse; and the one who knew all about aldermen and could do embroidery got a milk-white horse; and then they smeared the corners of their mouths with cod-liver oil, so that the words would come out pat. All the servants were down in the courtyard to see them mount their horses, when just at that moment up came the third brother; for there were three of them, though nobody ever took count of the third, because he wasn't a scholar like the other two. They called him Simple Simon.

"Where are you two off to in that get-up?" he asked.

"We're going to Court, to talk our way into favour with the Princess. Haven't you heard the proclamation that's been read out all over the country?" And then they told him all about it.

"Gosh! I mustn't miss this!" said Simple Simon. But his brothers laughed at him and rode away.

"Dad, let me have a horse!" cried Simple Simon. "I do so feel like getting married. If she'll have me, she'll have me; and if she won't, then I'll marry her all the same."

"What nonsense!" said the father. "I've no horse for you. Why, you never open your mouth. But look at your brothers—they are splendid fellows."

"If I can't have a horse," said the boy, "then I'll ride the billy-goat. It's my own, and it'll carry me all right, I know." Then he got astride the billy-goat, dug his heels into its sides and dashed off down the road. Phew! What a rate they went! "Look out! Here we come!" yelled Simple Simon, and his cries went echoing after him.

But his brothers rode on ahead in complete silence. They never said a word, because they had to turn over in their minds all the clever remarks they were going to make. It had to be most cunningly worked out, I can tell you.

"Tally-ho!" shouted Simple Simon, "here we are! Look what I found on the road," and he shewed them a dead crow he had picked up.

"You simpleton!" they said. "What are you going to do with that?"

"I shall give it to the Princess."

"Yes, do!" they answered, laughing as they rode on.

"Tally-ho! Here we are! Now look what I've found. You don't find that on the road every day."

The brothers turned round again to see what it was. "You simpleton!" they said. "Why, that's an old clog with the vamp missing. Is the Princess to have that as well?"

"Yes, of course," said Simple Simon; and his brothers only laughed at him and rode on till were a long way ahead.

"Tally-ho! Here we are!" shouted Simon. "My word! This is getting better and better. Tally-ho! This is grand!"

"What have you found this time?" asked the brothers.

"Oh, it's too good for anything," said Simple Simon. "Won't she be pleased, the Princess!"

"Ugh!" said the brothers. "Why, it's mud straight out of the ditch."

"Yes, that's just what it is," said Simple Simon, "and the very finest sort, too; it slips right through your fingers." And he filled his pocket with the mud.

But his two brothers rode on as hard as they could go, and the result was that they drew up at the city gate a whole hour ahead of him and found the suitors being given numbers in the order of their arrival. They were made to stand in rows, six in each file, and so close together that they couldn't move their arms. This was just as well, for otherwise they might have stabbed each other in the back, just because one was in front of the other.

The rest of the inhabitants all crowded round the castle, right up against the windows, so as to watch the Princess receiving her suitors; but as soon as ever one of them came into her presence, he was completely tongue-tied. "No good!" the Princess kept saying. "Skedaddle!"

Now it was the turn of the brother who knew the dictionary by heart. But he had clean forgotten it while he was standing in the queue; and the floor creaked under him, and the ceiling was all covered with mir-

rors, so that he saw himself standing on his head. At the window stood three clerks and an alderman, who all wrote down every word that was spoken, so that it could go straight into the newspaper and be sold for a penny at the street-corner. It was dreadful; and, what's more, they had made up such a fire that the stove was red-hot.

"It's very warm in here," said the suitor.

"That's because my father's roasting cockerels to-day," said the Princess.

"O-o-oh!" was all he could say, as he stood there. He hadn't expected a remark like that, and he was hoping to say something witty, "O-o-oh!"

"No good!" said the Princess. "Skedaddle!"—and away he had to go. After that the second brother came in.

"It's dreadfully hot in here," he said.

"Yes, we're roasting cockerels for dinner," said the Princess.

"I b-beg your—b-beg your—" he stuttered; and the clerks all wrote down "I b-beg your—b-beg your—"

"No good!" said the Princess. "Skedaddle!"

Now it was Simple Simon's turn. He came trotting in on the billy-

goat, right into the palace-room. "Why, it's as hot as blazes in here!" he said.

"That's because I'm roasting cockerels," said the Princess.

"Oh, I say, that's lucky," said Simple Simon. "So I suppose I can have a crow roasted, can't I!"

"Of course you can, quite easily," said the Princess; "but have you got anything to roast it in, for I've neither pot nor pan."

"But I have," said Simon. "Here's a cooker with a tin handle!" And he produced the old clog and popped the crow straight into it.

"It will make quite a meal," said the Princess. "But what shall we do for gravy?"

"I've got that in my pocket," said Simon. "I've enough and to spare." And he tipped a little mud out of his pocket.

"I do like that!" said the Princess. "You know how to answer; you can speak up for yourself, and you're the one I'm going to marry! But do you realise that every word we've been saying has been written down and will be in the papers to-morrow? Look there by the window—three clerks and an old alderman; and the alderman is the worst, because he doesn't understand a thing." Of course she said this just to frighten him. And the clerks all guffawed and made a great blot of ink on the floor.

"So these are the gentry?" said Simon. "Well, here's one for the alderman!" And he turned out his pocket and let him have the mud full in the face.

"Well done!" cried the Princess. "I could never have done that, but I'll soon learn." So in the end Simple Simon became King, with a wife of his own and a crown and a throne. And all this comes straight out of the alderman's newspaper; so it may not be perfectly true!